GOLD
HARVEST

by
GEORGE MAYFIELD

GOLD HARVEST

Published by

Green Magic
BCM Inspire
London WC1N 3XX

This edition published 2003

ISBN 09530460 0 1

WARNING

IT IS A CRIMINAL OFFENCE IN THE UNITED
KINGDOM PUNISHABLE BY IMPRISONMENT, TO
CULTIVATE, POSSESS, OR SUPPLY CANNABIS.
YOU SHOULD THEREFORE UNDERSTAND THAT THIS
BOOK IS INTENDED FOR PRIVATE AMUSEMENT,
AND NOT INTENDED TO ENCOURAGE YOU TO
BREAK THE LAW.

ACKNOWLEDGEMENTS

I would like to thank everyone involved with this
new edition of GOLD HARVEST. Especially Julie,
for the grief and hassle she's put up with, and Phil for his
patience (with Julie), Julia for design and Pete for his
photographs.

PREFACE

Since I first wrote the GREEN HARVEST book, I have been constantly asked to write an advanced version. One that deals with more detailed techniques, incorporating Hydroponics as well as the traditional soil growing methods.

I will try to keep this book as basic as is possible, without to much mind boggling, brain bending information. The reader will learn how to maximise the overall return, and how to obtain large plants from very basic gardens.

There will be photographs and illustrations along the way to show the reader what their gardens (plants) should look like. In my first book GREEN HARVEST, I tried to show the reader how to get the best return for their efforts, without any complicated data. I have read lots of grow books and, even if I say it myself, this first edition is a "gem" for the novice gardener. If you have read it and fully understood it, then this edition will show you how you could improve to a much higher standard.

Hydroponics seems to be the way to grow at present, so I will introduce you to some simple, but effective methods. There is a section catering for indoor and outdoor gardening. Both will give a detailed run down on the pro's and con's. Basically this book will be geared to the indoor gardener, although other than artificial light , there will be hardly any difference in the technique.

Everything you read in this book will be based upon 25 years of experience. I don't grow any more for the obvious reasons, one being that it's illegal, (and I got caught) the others are that I am trying to make my living selling legal information. I'll show you how to feed, transplant, flower, and grow to an expert standard. No fuss, no problems along the way (other than those you create for yourselves). Sensimilla is the main objective of this book. Everything else is just "incidental".

Whatever way you grow, the gardener must know something about the other simple but important data to enable them to produce top grade , blow your brain weed. Remember, cultivation is illegal at present. I don't know if the laws will be changed in the future, but if they do, you can be happy knowing that you have the knowledge to go ahead and produce your own blinding smoke.

The secret of success for anyone doing anything is to understand the basics, then progress with this knowledge to a higher standard. It's no good cutting corners trying to beat the time proven system. You'll come unstuck, that's guaranteed. Take your time, read and absorb. Imagine going up to a top prize winning gardener and telling them how to cut corners. They'll laugh at you because they haven't got where they are by trying to beat the natural system. These people (including myself) know that there is only one way, and that's the right way. As I told readers of my first book, I cut corners all the time, trying to beat the system.

I came well unstuck. I learnt through trial and error. Eventually, I cleared my brain and started again from scratch. God's way, nature's way, whatever you want to call it, it's the only way. Whether it be under artificial light or outside, you still have to obey the rules. Of course there are lots of little things you can do to improve your garden that nature doesn't do for you, but you'll still be, as I said earlier, following time proven techniques along the way.

As I said before, I won't be flooding your brain with any heavy going material, just some advanced techniques to help you further on your way.

I don't know why, but I still get a bit uptight with novice gardeners, who after one or two crops try to give it an *"I know everything, don't tell me"* attitude. I don't really call these people growers. I think of them as *"copy gardeners"* Anyone can get a nice balanced, well-grown garden if they want, but if they don't understand how it came about, (other than what they have read) then these people will in effect be *"cutting corners"*. The reason being that lack of understanding will inhibit any personal progress. This in turn will keep them at the same level for a long time. The secret is to read, listen, absorb and experiment for oneself. Log the findings and progress.

A knowledgeable gardener is the grower who can grow and cross the plants to obtain the fastest, largest, most powerful growing strain. An ability to produce all these factors, to get a strain of plant that meets one's personal requirements, is the key to successful growing.

CONTENTS

CHAPTER 1
Section 1   Marijuana (our plant)
Section 2   Security
Section 3   Indoors or outdoors?

CHAPTER 2
Section 1   Lights
Section 2   Preparing a grow room
Section 3   Photo period

CHAPTER 3
Section 1   Nutrients (Feeding, Water, P.H.)
Section 2   Soil (growing Mediums) Containers
Section 3   Seeds, Types, Germination

CHAPTER 4
Section 1   Taking cuttings (Clones)
Section 2   Sexing the Plants (Breeding)
Section 3   Sensimilla
Section 4   A basic growing study

CHAPTER 5
Section 1   Hydroponics
Section 2   Starting a Hydroponic Garden
Section 3   Garden Pests
Section 4   Deficiencies (Nutrient Over-fertilisation)

CHAPTER 6
Section 1 CO_2
Section 2   General Information

CHAPTER 7
Section 1   Harvesting
Section 2   Drying, Grading, Storing
Section 3   Last words

14

CHAPTER 1

Section 1

MARIJUANA (OUR PLANT)

Basically, Marijuana is just a weed. Not just any old weed though. It is capable of helping people in lots of ways. For a start it can make you laugh. Surely that alone is something special in this day and age! It can calm you down and relax you. It can make you appreciate yourself and the environment you live in. Besides being capable of helping you medically, it is also the only *"real"* plant of the future. Clothes, paper, baskets, curtains, furniture, in fact anything that trees are chopped down for (at an alarming rate) ,this plant can take over and help save nature from those money grabbing people who want to destroy our planet.

Without a doubt, this unobtrusive plant can really help us to create employment, and cheap alternative products (but just as good). It's fast turnover means that instead of waiting years to grow and chop down a beautiful tree, we can sow, grow, reap and produce virtually the same, every day of the year for practically nothing. Maybe this is the reason eh? The greedy money makers wouldn't be able to coin it in. Mind you, when the *"powers that be"* figure out a way of earning revenue from it, you can bet your last bud that they'll legalise it. Unfortunately money rules, people and the environment come second.

The life cycle of the Marijuana plant can be anything from 10-12 weeks to 6-7 months. All depends on what you want back from your labours. The younger the plant, the smaller the harvest.

What you require and when, depends on the individual grower. A fairly high resistance to most pests, with an inborn need to grow really fast, makes this plant interesting and fascinating to all growers. So just read this book and keep your fingers crossed that one day you might be allowed to legally grow with no hassle.

CHAPTER 1

Section 2

SECURITY

Whether the garden is legal or not, the grower will have to keep the crop away from all but the most trusted of people. Because it's illegal at the moment, the police have lots of ways of detecting the hidden garden. Infra red cameras, long range binoculars (outside growers) and their most important source of detection, the INFORMER. Indoor growing generally involves using high voltage lighting. This can make a significant difference to your electric bill. I know that if one pays the bills on time, no-one bothers you but, someone could recognise the high amount of power being used from what was a normal *"billed"* household and report this to the police. Paranoia? Maybe, but it's an instance of how you could be sussed out. Anyway, paranoia keeps you on your toes.

Keep all gardens away from any public view and where the smell cannot be detected by noses. Lofts, wardrobes, under the stairs may all be o.k. if you are sure no one is going to be going in or near them.

Only the grower would know the best place to suit their needs. Tell no-one! The desire to say *"I grew that"* is very high, because when people are praising something and it's your *'creation'* it's only natural to want to take the credit. DON'T! I could go on and on about security, but what's the point? I'm not saying for one moment you would, but imagine if you went out and spent all your hard earned cash on a *"set up"*, got it up and running and got caught because you didn't bother with proper security. Who's fault's that? There are also those smokers that can't be bothered to grow themselves. These people could nick it from you if you left it unattended, and they knew where your garden was. Legal or illegal, these gardens are a magnet. Use your head and get it right.

CHAPTER 1

Section 3

INDOORS OR OUTDOORS?

If the laws were changed and we could grow legally, I dare say the growing shops would go out of business. There are no systems in the world that can produce a better crop than those outside in the garden or greenhouse.

The reason being that the amount of top quality bush that could be grown in the garden would (could) come to tens of pounds. One plant alone grown in the British climate could easily produce 2lbs plus, with the same roughly of small leaf. Ten plants in the garden could give the grower anything from 10-20 pounds of pure bud, and roughly an equal amount of nearly as good small leaf (not shade leaf).

Use the shade leaf on the compost heap for the next season. These ten plants would use up a plot the size roughly of an area 15' x 6'. About a square metre each. Including seedling stage, vegetation stage, and flowering, the total time to grow these fully mature plants would be approx. 5 - 6 months. I remember a relative of mine back in the early 70's grew plants up to 11' - 12' high in his back garden. Neither he or I knew anything much about flowering and the photoperiod.

The next door neighbour asked him what those lovely bushes were that he was growing ,"Hawaiian Evergreens" he said. That made us laugh. Anyway these plants never got to the flowering stage because we never really knew what to do with them. Looking back with the knowledge I have now, these would have been the plants that could have produced large weights of bud (pounds). That's why you rarely (if ever) hear of a giant bush being grown. The sizes they can grow to, and the obvious security risk make growing these plants virtually impossible.

Now if you compare this outdoor crop to an indoor

one, the differences are plainly obvious. Firstly, assuming you are using just a small 560 watt set-up (1 x 400w sodium and 4 x 40 watt tubes). On top of that there's the initial outlay for the equipment. Forget the security side of it for now. We will assume growing is legal and we can grow how and where we like, (I wish). This small system is capable of returning anything up to about a pound + every eight weeks.

Experienced growers will get a little more, but because the system is small, the growing area won't be big enough to properly light and grow any crop over say 9 - 12 square foot. Obviously, the larger the system and garden you have the more you reap at the end of the cycle. So if you divide the eight week cycle into the 52 weeks of the year, you would in theory have the potential to grow 6 - 7 crops a year. If the grower used a three room system, one for seedlings, one for growing under Metal Halide and a flowering room with Sodium, then the return will be much better to some degree. I say this because if you grow larger plants to put in the flowering room, then the less plants you can use.

Plants need plenty of space to develop good "heads" from top to bottom. Everything has to be taken into account when planning an indoor garden. For a start the larger the garden, the more electricity you use. Then there's the extra work involved maintaining these fast growing plants. Only the grower will know what size garden they can successfully manage in a limited area.

The advantage of indoor gardens means that the grower could take fresh stock every couple of months as opposed to the one or two crops a year outside. The disadvantage being that the outdoor gardener would stroll down their garden once or twice a week to water or feed the plants. Then go back indoors to watch T.V. or sit in the sun, next to a bin liner sized bag stuffed with pounds of bud. The indoor grower would be constantly on the scene tending the garden. They will reap lots of ounces, the outdoor gardener will reap lots of pounds. Only trouble is who (if it were legal) would want to wait 5 months for a large crop for virtually nothing, when you could get one in 2 months? Personally, I know what I would do.

Although growing Marijuana is pleasurable, smoking it is much better. I feel the wait for an outdoor crop is more desirable because you can sit back and wait for another natural growing season to come to an end, and maintain your personal stash all year round with ease. Another disadvantage to growing outside is that if you made a mistake and grew too many plants, the return would be so large that you would have much more than you need, WHAT WOULD YOU DO WITH IT ALL? You wouldn't want to waste it would you? Seriously though, outside growing is THE BEST. Don't take my word for it, it's virtually free of running costs, hardly any real maintenance to talk of, and older mature plants normally have a higher T.H.C. level than quickly grown plants.

Ask anybody who has grown outdoors and they'll confirm what I write. I've got a picture in one of my books that shows a plant that was 19' tall and still growing. When it was chopped down and dried it gave up to 7 lbs of pure bud. ONE PLANT! Think about it.......... Indoors gives the grower a more hands on approach. They'll be with the garden virtually daily, watching it grow and bloom. The results will be really good and because of technology (lights, etc.) a regular crop will appear every eight weeks, hassle free. Outdoors you are more at the mercy of the elements but, even that can be overcome with foresight and planning.

The best way to grow is the way that suits you best. You decide what you want. Getting back to the 560 watt system I wrote of. If you were the *"bee's knee's"* and you managed somehow to pull, say even 1 1/2 lbs of bud every eight weeks, multiply this by the 6 - 7 crops you could grow in a year (52 weeks) and the potential yearly return could be from 7 - 10 lbs a year. That's great if that's how you like it. Only trouble is you'll be on the ball all year long to get at it.

Outdoors, growing a late season crop could quite

easily get you that amount with 6 - 8 plants. If you started cuttings under fluorescent and got them out at the right time, the grower could get two crops a year by harvesting an early season crop from say 10 plants altogether. Take the first crop from the plants round about April/ May, and by leaving some leaf and small bud on each plant, over the coming summer these same plants will regenerate, grow, and bloom into twice their previous size. Bud rot in the greenhouse is a bit of a problem to contain, if the growing season is allowed to extend into the early Winter months, (Sept./Nov.). Unless you have proper insulation and a correct air flow, the greenhouse will start to get a very high humidity. Once this happens the smallest rotting bud will quickly spread it's spores about, until the whole plant is affected.

The easiest way to help overcome this problem is to get it right from the beginning. Hang "bubble-wrap" all around the greenhouse and line the roof with it. Bury the bottom couple of inches in the soil. Cut a hole in the roof to enable you to open and close the vent. Make sure that you have good supply of air coming in from the bottom. Normally the door has a vent installed. If not, put one in!

Entry to the greenhouse would be through a flap made in the bubble-wrap. When planting, put a couple of plastic (1") tubes into the soil alongside the plants. During Summer months, the door and vent would be left open to enable the plants to get plenty of fresh circulating air. Humidity is easy to control. In the Winter, the damp atmosphere will push the humidity up to an undesirable level.

By using the bubble-wrap and covering the whole of the ground growing area with plastic, the grower will be able to contain the humidity. The plastic on the floor (growing area) will stop the damp rising into the greenhouse. The tubes I mentioned earlier would protrude through the plastic. This will enable the grower to feed and water the plants in a tidy and neat fashion, and reduce the humidity. A heater could be used, but only as a last resort. The *"wrap"* will stop the plants being affected by a sudden drop in temperature.

During the day, especially during the early Winter months, the wrap will keep the temperature at a reasonable level. Try to attain a good atmosphere for the plants using the materials I describe. If you do use a heater, DON'T use a paraffin heater. These are useless. The plants get affected by the fumes given off because they don't burn evenly.

A hot air blower regulated by a thermostat can be used, but don't let it blow directly on to the plants! These can be really expensive to use, but if you can afford it, go ahead. Now, the most important piece of equipment. A fan. This will enable the grower to keep humidity at a low level, and in turn bud rot wont come about. Fresh air from the greenhouse venting system will be thrown around the plants, ensuring a healthy disease free crop. Ordinary garden spiders will make a few webs in the greenhouse in the later months. They don't harm the plants and they help to keep down any other desirable pests. Get rid of them if you want, but it's not necessary,

If you do get bud rot (why ?) then as I said before, cut it out as quickly as possible. When cutting affected growth, take a look at where you've cut it and make sure that there isn't any *"black"* left. If there is, cut back until the remaining growth is clear. Crops can easily be grown well into the severest of Winter months in a greenhouse if you plan ahead. Sure, the growth rate will slow down some, and the final result wont be quite as much (weight), but overall the grower will be quite happy because the amount that can be grown outside in a greenhouse will compensate.

Also, you have to remember that the plants are governed by the natural photo-period, so unless you are using supplemental lights to extend the *"day time"*, most stock will have flowered by November at the latest.

A really well constructed greenhouse, with a proper heating and venting system, supplemented with electric light, can easily grow right throughout the Winter. I know about getting bud rot in the greenhouse. I got it myself. I

tried to cut some corners, Served me right, no more
though. I now know what is needed to be done to
eliminate it.. Please don't spoil your creations by neglect, it
hurts!

CHAPTER 2

Section 1

LIGHTS   (Fluorescent)

No plant can grow without light. The quality of the
light any plant receives, determines how it grows. Plants
have the ability to take light from the sun and convert it to
growth energy via it's leaves. This is called PHOTO-
SYNTHESIS. The natural light outdoors is made up of all
the colours of the spectrum. Plants take in and use the
different colour lights to determine how it will grow,
depending on what stage of it's life it is in.

Early in it's life a plant will mainly use the colours
towards the blue end of the spectrum to help it develop
and grow tall and strong. When flowering, a plant takes
light from the red end of the spectrum. When thinking of
what lights to buy, the grower must take all this into
consideration. Seedlings can be started under any light,
and flowering and vegetating plants the same. If you don't
put them under the right light at the proper time then,
although they'll grow and flower the final crop will be
smaller and lighter than those grown under the right light.

Power twist tubes have always been my favourite starter
tubes, but these can be quite expensive. The alternative
being WHITE LITE tubes. The difference between the two
is that although the spectrums are virtually the same, the
"twists" throw the light about more. This makes the
seedlings grow a little thicker and robust. Remember, a
healthy young strong plant will grow up much better than a
skinny stretched one. Experienced growers use a variety of
things to reflect light onto the plants. The difference then,
combined with their knowledge is very small. Power twists
help the grower. That's why I use them. Either way,
twists or White Lite tubes are the best to use for cuttings,
seedlings, etc.

Remember I said don't cut corners? Well, using White
Lite tubes as opposed to twists isn't cutting a corner. The

same results can be achieved from the ordinary tubes if you can be bothered to use adequate reflective materials. You still need reflective surfaces with the tubes, but as I said, it helps the grower to raise sturdy little plants. The twists are a kind of *"fail safe"*. Use tubes a minimum of 4ft unless space is really tight.

HIGH INTENSITY DISCHARGE LAMPS

Metal Halide and Sodium

METAL HALIDE'S

These are the lamps used by growers to raise their plants to the point of flowering. Just looking at these lights when working, tells you that they favour the blue end of the spectrum. As I said earlier ,the plants have to be given the right light at the right time to get the best return. Don't use these to raise seedlings or cuttings because unless you are experienced you'll probably end up with either burnt or elongated plants. Probably both. Anyway, you'll be burning money using these for young plants when tubes will do.

H.P.S (Sodium)

High Pressure Sodium lights are the main lights to use. Most growers use a two garden system with no need for a Halide. These lights favour the red end of the spectrum. Ideal for flowers, like the Halides they have the capability to penetrate deeply into the plants, helping to bud the whole stem rather than just the tops. Both types of lights come in lots of sizes from 150 watts up to 1000 watts. The most efficient are 400 and 1000 watt versions. Son-T bulbs are the best on the market to date.

There are several other light systems for sale that are developed for plant growth. The grower must make up their own mind as to what ones they would use. As long as it's the right lamp for the right occasion, then you'll be

O.K. Most grow shops are run by reputable and knowledgeable people. Check them out and see what they say. Some will try to sell you a crappy unit purely because they have a bigger *"mark up"* on that particular model. Pay a bit more and get a decent light that will efficiently do the job it's intended for. Any other bulb is a waste of time really. Mercury vapour, low pressure sodium's for example. The bulbs have a life of a couple of years before they start to lose their efficiency. Never the less, changing the bulb yearly keeps your crop under peak lighting conditions. All come with their own starter gear. Use them properly and you should never experience any problems.I honestly think that the Sodium bulbs are just as good as the Halide's for the purpose of *'bringing them on'.*

REFLECTORS AND LIGHT BALANCERS

To help maximise efficiency, lights can be greatly helped by the use of reflectors and balancers. Use mirrors, reflective mylon sheeting or flat white walls to reflect the light back to the plants. This really helps to promote growth. With a balancer moving your light around the garden, combined with good reflective material, a significant increase in weight and quality will result.

When figuring out how much light is needed to grow, the reader must first work out how much space there is to illuminate. The way to do it is as follows:- Let's say that you have an area of 1 square metre to play with. Well this is approximately 9 - 10 square foot. The ideal light per square foot is 40 watts, so a 400 watt light would give you maximum lighting. You can grow with as little as 15 - 20 watts per square foot, but this will greatly reduce the potential of the garden. Don't cut corners!
Using smaller lights supplemented with a couple of tubes and light bulbs is another waste of time. An inefficient spectrum and a bundle of cables to contend with, who needs that? Buy a nice efficient light at the start and you'll have eliminated any problems to do with lighting.

CHAPTER 2

Section 2

PREPARING A GROW ROOM

After figuring out where you will set up your grow room (See security) and working out the size (space) you'll be using ,the first job will be to construct a chamber. The best stuff to use for the walls is the white boards that can be bought in most superstores. A nice matt white plastic finish, dead straight ,waterproof and easy to wipe down to keep it clean.

After cutting the boards to size, fix them together with the little fixing blocks specially made for the job. Make sure the height is high enough to allow for the lamp and the eventual height the plants will reach. A novice grower will need to have a room at least 6' high until experience shows them how to contain the plants height. Once the grower can do this, then it's possible to have a lower room. Obviously if one was growing under several large lights, the room would be bigger therefore creating the need for more light spread. You're always going to need at least 18" - 24" distance between light and crop. Bear this in mind when constructing your room.

Make sure that all the seams between your construction material are sealed. Use thick carpet tape or something similar. As you know, it's so important that light doesn't reach the plants during the dark period.

An adequate ventilation system must be incorporated into the room. The need for a good supply of fresh air is essential for good growth. The easiest way to vent a room is to place a 6" x 9" plastic vent into the bottom of the room with a light proof cover, and another at the top. If the room is in a warm situation, another should be placed to let the rising hot air out. Ideally, a small 4" - 6" bathroom extractor would be put in the top. Connect this to a tube or whatever, and direct the pungent air to a "safe zone". A tube from the middle of a roll of carpet, or a piece of plastic drainpipe does the job.

Connect the extractor fan to an ordinary household central heating thermostat. Now as you know, an ordinary thermostat works when the room gets too cold. We don't want this to happen, so you find an electrician to show you how to wire the thermostat in reverse. What happens then is that when it gets too hot (more than 70 - 75 degree's) the extractor cuts in and draws the hot air out, and in turn the fresh air comes in through the lower vent.

An example of how to wire a standard room thermostat in reverse is shown below.

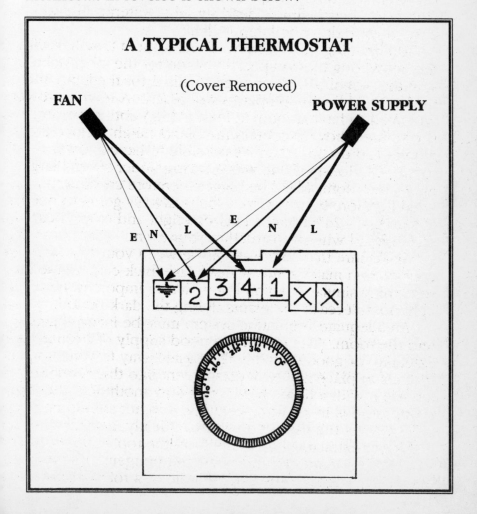

Leave the thermostat switched on all the time. The minimum temperature would be controlled by a thermostatically controlled heater. Set these two up to maintain a minimum of 50 - 55 degree's for the night cycle and a maximum of 70 - 75 degree's for the day cycle. It might take a while to find a happy medium before the best temperatures are achieved, but it's really worth the effort. A min/max thermometer helps greatly. If the room is built in a cold place then the need for insulation comes in. Use 1" or 2" polystyrene sheeting to line the box out, or put it all over the outside. It's up to you. Either way use the insulation for a pot base, covered with a clear plastic decorators sheet. This allows the white floor to reflect, and protects anything underneath from water spillage.

Make sure all electric cable and fittings are fixed up out of the way. Safety first o.k. The top of the room should be strong enough to support the light fitting, which would be connected to a pulley. The entrance to the room should be made light proof. Go to a car breakers yard and get yourself some rubber seal that goes round the door openings. Fix this to your door and round the door entrance, and sort out a secure fastening device. When you're satisfied that you've sorted the light problem, get a most trusted person to lock you in and see if there's any light coming in. If everything is O.K., the grow room is now ready to take the plants.

The cutting or seedling box should be constructed once again according to the room available. 4 x 4 foot fittings fit nicely under a 2 foot x 4'6" cover. Under this would be enough room to give the grower at least 18" height for the young plants. Construct the box as you would the grow chamber. Line it out with plastic sheeting. This room doesn't have to be light proof because the baby plants will be in a vegetating state. Therefore, unless security is at risk, just make sure that you create a box that has a high humidity, 80 degrees is O.K.

The plastic sheeting, the water in the pots, should bring the humidity up to the right amount. Place a small vent top and bottom. You are now in control. Put a small thermometer gauge in, and the box is now ready to use.

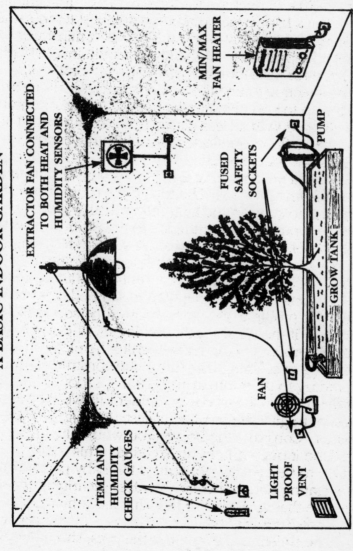

A BASIC INDOOR GARDEN

EXTRACTOR FAN CONNECTED TO BOTH HEAT AND HUMIDITY SENSORS

MIN/MAX FAN HEATER

FUSED SAFETY SOCKETS

PUMP

GROW TANK

TEMP AND HUMIDITY CHECK GAUGES

FAN

LIGHT PROOF VENT

ALL ELECTRICAL EQUIPMENT SHOULD BE CONNECTED TO FUSED SOCKETS BEFORE CONNECTING TO MAINS POWER/TIMERS. WATER AND ELECTRICITY DON'T MIX. TAKE CARE.

29

CHAPTER 2

Section 3

PHOTOPERIOD

To enable the plants to bloom, they must have at least 8 - 14 days of unbroken night cycle to initiate flowering. Indoors, we set the timer, close the door and leave it at that. Outside, we are governed by the natural photoperiod. Understanding the photoperiod is really vital to the grower. Normally indoors, we set the timer to turn the light on and off every 12 hours. This is normally the recommended cycle given to initiate most stock to flower. The trouble is that unless you have proven seed/cuttings from a reputable source, you wont know whether or not you are getting the maximum return in the shortest time.

Let me explain, plants come from all different parts of the world, some are gigantic resinous buggers that wouldn't get a flea stoned. Others are small insignificant plants with a devastating *"high"*. Some flower in 5 weeks, some in 10 to 12 weeks. As time went by people crossed these plants to get the best characteristics from them. The large gigantic plant I mentioned might flower in 5 weeks. The other would flower in 10 - 12 weeks. The idea is to cross them and get a fast flowering plant that is high in T.H.C. (power) levels.

Some plants are crossed to get a plant that grows large and strong with another that will help it keep its character, but only grow to half the size. These plants initially were influenced by the amount of day v night they receive in their native habitat. When they are crossed the resulting plants (hybrids) would be a mixture of two different photoperiods. An example being a strain near the equator crossed with a strain from , say Europe.

How do you know how much light v dark they need to flower? As I said, 12 dark v 12 night gets most plants to flower within 2 weeks max. Unfortunately unbeknown to you, although they'll flower and produce nice crops, how would you feel after flowering for eight weeks, if someone told you that you could have had them *"flowered off"* in 6 weeks, and on top of that more return? Well this could quite easily happen if you didn't have expert advice on your seed/cutting stock. You must try to find out the origin of your stock to enable you to give the best photoperiod to suit.

A way to find out is to set the photoperiod for 12 and 12 hours respectively. If all the plants (assuming they are from the same stock) haven't started to flower inside 7 - 14 days, turn the light off for 13 hours versus 11 light. They should all flower profusely. If you don't get it right, the plants get slightly confused. They don't know whether to keep growing or flower. Because the light cycle is nearer to equal (12 x 12) they tend to end up flowering after about 2 weeks.

If they had been flowered under say a 13 dark versus 11 day regime, they would have sussed that flowering time is here straight away. No plant energy would have gone towards partial vegetation growth, thus slowing the flowering process down. They would be receiving the maximum light they need to sustain fast healthy flower growth. In turn this would let the plant get to maturity a lot quicker, (say 6 weeks), and the return would be more because growing time would have been spent just flowering ,instead of a mixture of flowering and vegetation confusion initially.

Understanding your plants needs, greatly improves the harvest. When a grower buys their seed from a grow shop, 12 versus 12 is recommended, because as I said, eventually (up to 8 weeks) the plants flower beautifully. Maybe they don't know about the effects of a proper photoperiod or they can't be bothered to tell you. Maybe if you yourself don't understand it, then you would be unlikely yourself to ask the shopkeeper about it. Take a tip from me, unless you know what you're doing, or you know a good knowledgeable gardener, the only way to find out the facts is to do it yourself.Most Dutch Hybrid seed is geared to flower with a 12 v 12 regime. I had some blinding results.

Then I started using the old grey matter and went about trying a few different photoperiod times. An instance being Haze X Skunk No 1. The recommended times were 12 v 12. Flowers maturing in 9 - 12 weeks. I put the same under a 13 night versus 11 day and flowered them in 8 weeks. I was well happy with the outcome and, I saved 2 - 3 weeks. This spare time was used to start flowering the next lot. Quite a saving over the course of a growing year. Never set the night cycle too short. This can result in male flowers forming, and a loss in weight. Use the rule of thumb I told you about. If they haven't all started to flower inside 2 weeks max., then set the photoperiod 1 hour more towards *"night"*. In fact set the photoperiod for any Hybrid seed at 12½ hours night versus 11½ hours day to begin with. This should reasonably satisfy most growers.

For those growing outside in the green house there is the option of extending the photoperiod with supplemental lighting. When the Summer nights are drawing in the grower could add sufficient light for a couple of hours, thus ensuring a *"complete"* crop.

Do you know that as long as the plants are getting enough light during the natural day, they can be grown to maturity with something as simple as a couple of candles in jam jars, for that extra couple of hours every night?

It's true, OK, so the light isn't as intense as natural or proper light but, the fact is the plants are still experiencing light, and this is enough to sustain them. A slightly smaller crop will result, but nevertheless a mature, fully grown one.

I grew some Afghani in my back garden. Most of it had started to flower except one. This particular plant started flowering about six weeks later than the others. *"Weird"* I thought, until I realised that it was getting light every night from our back room. I should have realised earlier, no excuse, I wasn't thinking. This plant really blew the others away. Great big heads. Lovely high.

I was really lucky though because the Winter was

extremely mild that year, and it wasn't cut down until mid December. The back room light kept it going until the plant naturally flowered in its own time. Lucky old me, eh?

Original uncrossed seed stock should be carefully monitored to find the most suitable photoperiod to obtain maximum return and minimum flowering time.

CHAPTER 3

Section 1

NUTRIENTS (feeding)

As you probably know, if you stuck a Marijuana plant under a 100 watt light bulb or on a window-sill, fed it with a general fertiliser, tap water, and in a stuffy climate, it would try it's heart out to survive, and it will! These plants are so hard to kill, that unless you're a totally useless gardener they will grow and do the best they can with whatever is available to them. When they are looked after properly, they not only survive, they go berserk. Instead of skinny elongated large leafy plants, you'll end up with lush, large buds (heads).

Everything depends on what you do for them, as to how they repay you. .Nutrients these days are sold in lots of different formulas, for the needs of all different kinds of plants. Finding the right ones for your plants isn't hard if you understand what they want. Marijuana is a Nitrophile. It will take copious amounts of **N** (nitrogen) throughout it's life.

Plants need Nitrogen to form leaves to catch the sun.(Light). Nitrogen also helps the plant grow large and lush. **P** (phosphorous) is used by the plant to help it during germination and it's infancy stage. Also it is vitally important for flower formation.

K (potassium) is necessary for helping the plant settle down and form properly. Also needed for good flowers. To get the most from the plants, these nutrients must be fed at the right time with the proper amounts.

When growing a vegetation plant, a general fertiliser high in nitrogen would be used. When flowering, a formula would be used with very little or no **N** at all. The reason being that you don't want to promote leaf growth, just thick dense buds. All good garden centre's sell general tomato fertilisers that would give the grower a reasonably good vegetation plant. Then you get to the flowering stage and try to find a fertiliser with no nitrogen. Nigh on impossible.

Hydroponics grow shops sell liquid fertilisers. Grow and Bloom. These work excellently. Unfortunately, you must make a decision before using this fertiliser. Most of it is chemical. Even if you flush your plants out for the last few weeks, they have still been fed chemicals You can taste it. I don't care what anyone says. Even the best grown grass has that distinctive metallic taste, albeit, very little.

This fertiliser sells well because it gives great results (weight) and it eliminates the need to "knock up" your own formula. Some hydroponic shops sell organic formulas, but you'll pay extra for it. You must decide. Buy the basic ingredients and make it yourself for pennies, or pay someone else who has took the time to formulate it, and sell it in concentrated form, for pounds. If you can drag on a joint and not taste anything other than natural sweetness, this is the right way to grow. (See washing out, chapter 4). Novice and *"copy gardeners"* will use these chemical formulas because it gets them results and allows them to not think. Put it this way, what food tastes the best, organically grown or mass produced chemically grown? You know don't you? Grass is no different.

The way to feed your plants is to give the vegetating (mother) plants a start with a good, well balanced general organic fertiliser, one high in **N.P.K**. A couple of weeks before you decide to take cuttings or flower, cut the feed in half. This won't hurt the plants in any way. Go and buy a box of super-phosphate **(P)** and a box of potassium **(K).** Make up the feed at this given rate and you'll have a really good return. Firstly the **(P)** mix 60 gram's in 2 gallons of water, with 40 grams of potassium **(K).** This will give you a good but high balance of the two major nutrients necessary for a good, high-yield crop. The plants will be sustained through flowering without any nitrogen because you have fed it in it's veggy stage with plenty.

Sometimes in it's life, a plants lower older leaves start

to yellow. This is normal, but if you know that you've fed the plants properly, with the right amounts of fertiliser, and a rapid yellowing of the plants start, the normal school of thought would be to *"green"* them up again with more nitrogen - wrong! The problem is definitely most likely to be a deficiency of magnesium. <u>Magnesium Sulphate</u>, generally known as Epsom salts and sold in all garden centres. Feed as per instructions and in a few days you'll see a great improvement. Depending on what growing medium you are using, as long as it has a good balance of the minor nutrients, and a regular balanced feed of the major ones ,no real problems should be experienced. With the latest chemical formulas you get a high but balanced concentration of feed. Try *"pumping"* them with more than you should and you'll end up smoking something very bitter. That's why the instructions are very exact. With organic fertiliser, the grower can *"pump"* the plants full to the limit and not spoil them. Don't do this though, until you are 100% confident your plants are growing in conditions ideal enough to take it, and you know what you are doing.

WATER

Firstly before you grow or feed any Marijuana plant, you must get to know your water. Sounds a bit stupid doesn't it? Get this wrong and any effort you've made to get the fertiliser right will be a waste of time. I'll explain. Grass needs to be fed with water that is acid. About 6.3 - 6.8. Most household water is high (alkaline) round 7.5 - 8.0. Get a water tester, fill a 1 or 2 gallon bucket with water and see what it tests at. Go to your local grow shop and buy some "down". Aquarium shops stock similar stuff to enable you to get the p.h.right for certain kinds of fish. It's unlikely that you'll need to get anything to raise the P.H. because most household water is high. Apply the *"down"* as instructed, wait ½ an hour and see what it reads by re-testing. Add your fertiliser and see if that makes any difference to the reading. If it does, adjust it to come into the desired range.

Try to fill the bucket every time you use it, so that it has been standing for a least a day. Nice warmish, tepid water is the best to use. Straight from the tap is too cold. Think about it, what would you like to be drenched in, cold hard water or nice warmish tepid water? A plant is a living thing, and like us reacts as we would! Now I'll tell you something that is really important. When plants send out all them little roots to collect water, they need to be able to suck it through easily. This enables the plant to get it's feed into the system with no hassle. A combination of too much fertiliser mixed with untreated water will clog up all the thousands of little root canals necessary for fast overall growth.

I met an Englishman living in Holland who was a friend of a close pal of mine.This man was the "business" when it come to growing the "puff". He told me that if he could only control one element in the growing procedure, it would be the P.H. of the water. The man was standing there with a bag of absolutely beautiful grass that he'd grown. He knew what he was talking about for sure. He explained to me what I've just told you. If the plant isn't able to take in all that it needs, in the right quantity, at the proper time in it's life, then everything else in the growing chain would be affected. Everything started to fall into place. Water management from now on would be a priority to enable everything else to work. Rainwater is near neutral P.H. (7.0). So it still needs a bit of help. Don't cut corners if you want good results. Never put water/feed on the plant, just around it.

Young plants (seedlings & cuttings) seem to grow much better if you don't water them from the top of their containers. Place the starter pots or whatever you are using in trays and fill the trays with the correct amount. They will suck up the fluid from the bottom as they need it. Once again, do this correctly from the beginning and overall the plants will benefit right through their growing season. A much sturdier, stocky plant will result.

CHAPTER 3

Section 2

SOIL (growing mediums)

When any plant is growing it needs to be able to breath underground. Hard soil with aeration problems will definitely hinder growth. The ideal medium for any plant, not just grass, is one that has a crumbly texture, with all the right trace elements in it. The size of a plant and its buds are determined by the size of its root ball underneath. When the root system can literally fall through the growing medium, sucking up the vital fluids with ease then this will send a signal to the vegetable matter above ground that it can get large. A strong robust plant cannot be expected to grow from a small clogged up root system.

Fisons have formulated a soil that is perfect for seedlings/cuttings right through to flowering. F.1 It's a beautiful loamy lightweight soil with all the minor nutrients added. Mix this 50/50 with Perlite, put it on top of a few pebbles to assist drainage and away you go. Good general compost mixes, even grow bag contents are a smashing medium to use. Mix them all with Perlite, try not to use any mix that is mostly peat because it tends to be a bit strong for the plants. You must try and get a medium that is low in the major nutrients because if you don't, when you add your formula to it , you wont know for sure how much you're using. That why I preferred Fisons F.1. mix. No major nutrients. I was in control.

The faster a plant can spread it's roots, the faster it fills the starter pot. At the first sign of roots popping out of the drainage holes, you pot it up to the next size. By doing this you end up in the final flowering pot with a root ball big enough to sustain large plants. This is how you would maximise your return, (all other factors being right).

CONTAINERS AND STARTER CUBES

When the grower starts a seed or takes a cutting, it would be placed in a small 2" - 3" pot or a Rockwool cube. Immediately the first sign of a tap root showing the grower would pot up to a slightly larger pot. Say a 4" one, and again as the roots appear, they would straight away be placed in a 5" pot and so on, until the plants have grown up to the size you require. The larger, more compact root system you have, determines how the plant will grow above ground. It's amazing really how many growers overlook this really important factor. To them it's just what grows above ground that matters. Then after careful tending and nursing they end up a bit disappointed because they only took a small crop for their labour. Let me explain.. When a tap root goes out it has only one thing on it's mind. That is to find food and oxygen to feed the plant. From this root comes other roots with the same objective. If they are allowed to "bolt" the root ball grows o.k. but not as compact as one would like. A small pot will stop the tap root from going too far, and the other roots would grow faster and quicker, so as to make up for the confinement the tap root is experiencing. As soon as you pot up to the next size, you tease the mass of small root ball a little, and in turn this will quickly fill the next size pot and so on.

If the grower was transplanting from say a 3 litre rose pot to a bucket (1 gallon), you would expect the root ball in the 3 litre pot to be virtually packed. A root ball the size of a large fist would hardly warrant going into any pot larger than a 6" (1½) litre pot. The larger the root system is, the larger the top plant will grow. When the plant has a signal from it's roots that there is plenty of matter below ground, it forms a large plant accordingly. I've seen plants 2' tall, covered in large fan leafs, about 4" - 6" apart. These plants when they had finished flowering gave a very small return because the root ball was only big enough to sustain a straggly plant. The same plant if it had been potted up properly, could have produced a much greater return of the desired bud.

When you are starting your seedlings or cuttings use a soil/perlite mixture. 25% soil and 75% perlite. Rockwool cubes are neat and efficient, especially for the Hydroponics grower, but believe me, the root doesn't grow as fast and dense as it does in the same way as the soil grower. Usually though, Rockwool is used mostly by the fast turnover Hydroponics gardener. When growing for size remember the importance of the root ball. Combine this knowledge with what you know about water, light, feed etc., and you'll end up with sturdy little plants, covered from the base of the branches to their tops with lush growth. Then, when you come to flower, your plants will have hardly (if any) wasted space between the shoots. This in turn will ensure the buds will all grow close together and form the large head that you desire.

SOIL - P.H.

Once again, like water, the soil that you use must have an ideal P.H. of between 6.3 – 7.0. This combines with the water to help the plant take in it's sustenance without any hassle. If you are using soil that doesn't fall into the desired P.H. range then you must adjust it. Go to your local garden store and buy the necessary additive. Adjust as per instructions. This isn't hard to do and you don't have to be too green fingered to achieve it. Believe me though, if you want to maximise your return for your efforts, this is one of the things you must also get right. A small soil test kit will give you a pretty precise measure of your acidity or alkalinity. Rockwool has a P.H. of about 7.5. It needs to be soaked for 24 hours in an acidic solution (5.5 - 6.0), to enable it to stabilise at an acceptable level when in use.

CHAPTER 3

Section 3

SEEDS

With so many different strains on the market today, the grower would have a difficult time making up their mind as to which ones to grow. There is a choice between Hybrid and original uncrossed seed. Only the grower knows what they like. Normally though to begin with, most growers want the fastest and largest return plants. This is only natural. Taste and bouquet are important too. The *"high"*, does it last, or fall of the shelf pretty quick? Do you want a smoke that will allow you to stroll down the market without a *"lead weight"* feeling at the back of your head? A nice trippy kind of smoke that sticks your gums to your teeth and make you grin like a Cheshire cat? Or a powerful smoke to listen to the Pink Floyd, and be unable to move?

You can get any kind of *"hit"* if you use the stock that is most suitable for yourself. Breeding different characteristics from seed enables the grower to create their own *"personal high"*. Most hybrid seed used today was originally created from RUDERALIS crossed with the SATIVA and INDICA plants. The RUDERALIS is generally a low potency plant but it flowers very quickly. By crossing these with the Indicas and Sativas, fast flowering potent strains were obtained. Hybrids are generally a much faster, sturdier growing grass than the uncrossed strains. They have a good resistance to disease, pests, etc. These are the preferred stock used by most growers. Don't write off the natural uncrossed strains. If you can be bothered to grow and develop them properly, I believe that these are just as rewarding.

SATIVAS - Colombian, Mexican, Jamaican.

INDICAS - Afghani, African.

These plants are probably the most common ones we hear of.

You've probably heard of Durban Poison, Red Beard, these are strains of developed original stock. The photoperiod can vary greatly with different seed. It all depends on where they originated. The day and night regime in that particular area, determines how long they need to flower and how much night versus day. (Read photoperiod).

Below is a chart of seeds and their characteristics, flowering times etc., indoors or out:-

SKUNK

A Hybrid plant that breeds true. 75% Sativa and 25% Indica, grows 6' - 9' high. A very strong plant that flowers in 12 hours of light, maturing in about 8 weeks, outdoors it ripens about the end of September, very sweet with a good taste, high return.

SKUNK NO 1

Very similar characteristics, 75% - 25% Sativa/Indica. Not very good for outdoor growing, 12 v 12 light times, 7 - 9 weeks flowering, high return.

HAZE

A pure (Sativa). A very sweet smell with a very potent *"high"*, flowers in about 14 weeks under 12 v 12 light times. Outside they flower at the end of September with 13 hours of dark, high return.

AFGHANI NO 1

Another pure breed. Blow your brain *"high"*, very resinous, with large wide leaves, flowers with 12 v 12 in about 8 weeks, outside it flowers by the end of October, large return.

CALIFORNIA ORANGE X SKUNK NO 1

A Hybrid. Sativa/Indica. Mostly Indica. A nice sweet taste with a lovely *"high"*, not recommended for outdoors, 12 v 12 flowers these plants in 7 - 8 weeks, a nice mix, and a reasonable return.

DURBAN POISON

Sativa, a pure bred plant with a high strength, can be grown in or out, flowers in about 7 - 8 weeks indoors, and outside it flowers around the end of August or September. High return.

Don't if you can help it, use seed from that illicit deal. The reason being that there's a good chance it wont belong to the weed it's with. A lot of dealers throw in any old seed as a "make weight". If you know for sure that the seed is definitely from the grass you've smoked, and you like it, then grow that. Not only will you know that you'll have smoke you like, it will be better than the original. The reason being that you've bought seeded buds and you'll be growing *"Sensi"*, unseeded buds, (unless you want to breed). Use nice large fat seeds, ones with a nice colour e.g. Dark brown, greyish or mottled. These stand a better chance of germination. Keep all seeds in a film canister, and throw them in the freezer. Don't keep them too long, they *do* lose potential in time.

If you have selected a good, healthy seed, then germination should be no problem. If you have your own method of germination and it suits you then carry on. The best way to germinate any good seed is to place them on top of 2 or 3 pieces of loo paper. Cover them with the same. Add water until saturated and pour off any excess. Put them in a warmish airy closet or whatever, and wait anything from 2 to 4 days. <u>Don't let it dry out!</u> The very moment you see them start to split, get them into the starter pot/cube. Place them in the starter cube/soil at about ¼" max. Cover with cling film. Immediately the seeds pop the surface, take of the cling film. Even if only one has "shown" don't worry. If they are all from the same source, then the others will make an appearance very soon after.

Stopping the plants stretching out of all proportion is achieved easily. There is no need to water deeply because at this point there's no root to speak of. Just use a fine mist spray (an old window cleaner bottle) and lightly dust the surface. Try to imagine how much water it would take to water the top ½". The more water you give (remember p.h.) the faster it will grow. Find a balance between root and top growth and keep the light (if growing indoors) as near as 2" from the tops of the plants.

Adjust the light distance if you need to, but generally fluorescents wont really harm the plants. You'll have to keep an eye on them because the warm light will dry the medium out quickly. This results in the plant either dying or warping. Then the plant has to spend valuable growth energy getting itself back together. The first 3 - 5 days are so critical. Perfect this technique and you should experience very little hassle.

Try not to use starter pots less than 3" - 4" deep to begin with. (Avoid seed trays). The reason being that when the tap root goes out,. if it isn't able to get some distance before hitting something (bottom of pot) then there's a chance that you will end up with a MALE plant. Who wants that? Root restriction when young, is one of the reasons that we get a lot of male plants. I read in a book that scientific experiments in Russia showed that female development is restricted a lot because of this. Use the right pot. Don't let the seedling go through an entirely wet and dry cycle. A fine balance of moist instead of dry is ideal. Then when the pot starts to get root bound, the grower should have a cutting of 2 - 3 weeks old with a large root system and a sturdy youngster above. (See containers). Remember this plant can grow a couple of inches a day in the right conditions. Adjust the light accordingly.

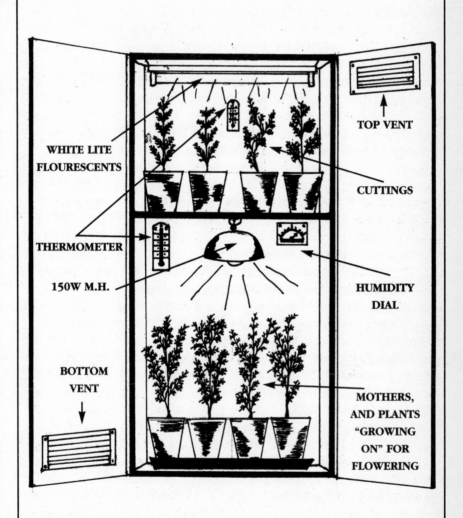

TOP VENT

WHITE LITE FLOURESCENTS

CUTTINGS

THERMOMETER

150W M.H.

HUMIDITY DIAL

BOTTOM VENT

MOTHERS, AND PLANTS "GROWING ON" FOR FLOWERING

A BASIC CLOSET NURSERY

CHAPTER 4

Section 1

TAKING CUTTINGS (Clones)

A garden can be started with one seed, and assuming the strain is to the growers liking, can be used for years. Grow the seed into a vegetating plant (a mother) and take a constant supply of cuttings from it. When the mother plant has been cannibalised enough, flower it off if you want, and produce another mother from one of its cuttings. Because of their genetic make-up, these plants will always be the same in power (THC) and growing potential. These cuttings are called clones. To take a cutting, the grower would take an active growing shoot and cut it about 3" - 4" long from the middle of the nearest internode to that length. An internode is a joint where the leaves and stem join. Cut it crossways at an angle so that you leave more exposed area than a straight cut. The reason for this is that there is more growing surface to promote root growth. A week or so prior to taking cuttings the grower would cut the Nitrogen feed by at least half. This helps them to root more easily. Use a good rooting powder, or Bio-Roota gel. The gel seems to produce better results. Remove the bottom set of leafs and cut the remaining ones in half (crossways). You do not want to touch the small leaf growing round the shoot if you can help it. The more leaf the cutting has, the better chance there is of success.

The reason being that the more leaf surface a plant has the more energy it can take in to promote growth. Place the cutting in its starting pot or rockwool cube, up to the next set of leaf. About 1½" - 2". Make sure that the soil or whatever you are using isn't constantly flooded. This young plant has a hard time ahead of it. Plenty of Oxygen round its roots and a nice humid atmosphere really help it. Water it sympathetically.

I would recommend strongly that you don't use

anything other than root stimulator to sustain the plant at this stage. Once the plant has started to root successfully, the grower would then introduce it to a complete feed. Maxicrop Liquid Seaweed with a N.P.K. of 5.5.5 is ideal. The clones would be placed in the cutting box and placed 3" - 4" inches from the lights. Its very hard to water these little plants without getting any on the leaf and stems. Especially if there is a lot to do.

Go to the chemist or your local vet and buy yourself a large (50 mil) syringe. No need for the needle, knock up your mix and feed each plant precisely with the same amount. You can direct the fluid exactly where you want it without splashing or flooding the plant (Don't forget the water P.H). I know it's a bit *"over the top"*, but these little things really help a plant to get on its way. It's to your advantage to give the plant the best start you can. To begin with, for about the first 6 - 8 days you'll be attending your cuttings at least twice a day. You don't want them to dry out and you can't give them lots of water, because of what I said about the need for lots of Oxygen around the roots.

The lights soon dry out the small amounts of liquid you give them quite quickly. The light in the cutting box should really be on for 24 hours. 18 hours is o.k. but you'll get at least 25% more growth overall with 24. The difference in electric costs is so small that it's not worth bothering with. These plants would be grown as described in chapter 3, section 2. If you are going to have a fast turnover garden the plants would be sustained on the 5.5.5. formula until they were about 4 - 5 weeks old. By this time they should be about 8 - 10 inches high with lots of growth. Remember, the right amount of fluid and a correct light to plant distance will ensure good strong stock.

The clones usually root between 1 - 2 weeks. Once you see new growth, this will be a sure indicator of success. It's from this point that you age the plants. So 1-3 weeks of rooting and 4 - 5 weeks of "growing on" will make these plants about 7 - 8 weeks old when they would be ready for the flowering box. If you are going to use a Metal Halide to grow them even bigger before you flower them, then they would be taken from the cutting box and placed under the Halide at about 5 -6 weeks old. Plants that are 6 -7 weeks old when put under the sodium will have grown side branches and leaves. Next to these leaf stalks, new growing shoots with tiny leaves will be present. Remove the side branches, leave on all but the large fan (shade) leaves. Don't take off any of those small leaves that have grown between the stem and branches. This gives the grower more room for lots of plants to grow. Side branches take up valuable grow space, and also they shade the bottoms of the plants. The idea is to get a large cola (head) from the soil to the top of the plant. Don't worry if they look a bit sad, within 2 weeks of flowering they'll start to shape up. 4 weeks and they are really on their way. After six weeks they should be about 2 - 3 inches thick and buds all the way up the stem. The last couple of weeks is when the plant goes into overdrive and really fattens up.

The plants that went under the Halide would either be "grown on" as they are until they reach the desired size, and then they would be flowered. At about 4 weeks of age, or when the plants had at least 3 - 4 sets of leafs, the grower would pinch out the top growing shoot. This quickly promotes side growth. This is how you would make your "mother" plant. Don't pinch out too much too often because you'll end up with small growing tips. OK for a mother plant, but not for a plant being grown for large buds Also this is how you would control the plant's height in a limited space. The plants would have been gradually *"potted up"* until they reach the desired size before flowering. Set the lights about 18" from the top of the plants and away you go.

A good oscillating fan will help to throw Oxygen about the room. So with the right light, growing medium and an adequate Oxygen/ventilation turnover, the plants will flourish. Don't place the lights too near to the plant tops because you'll burn them. As long as your light covers all the garden evenly, that's all that matters. Getting the distance right, stops the plants from bolting (stretching). The idea is to have a happy medium. It doesn't matter how good you are or how much experience you have, you'll always have one or two plants that outgrow the rest. As I said you could cut the top off, but this will promote unwanted side growth. (Unless you're growing large plants).

Keeping all the cuttings at the right height, helps the grower to feed and maintain the plants a lot easier. You'll be forever moving the light to compensate, or you'll be raising the rest up on blocks or whatever. This is no good. The easiest way is to carefully take a piece of cloth and form a loose loop. This would be placed near the top of the plant and you would bend it over until it was the same height as the rest. Not only does this enable you to promote even growth all over the room, it also makes the *"tied over"* plants grow quicker. When the growing tip is pulled down, this gives a signal to the rest of the plant to quickly get that small lower growth to get a *"move on"*.

Constant reaching into the growing room to adjust plant height means that you'll probably be knocking the other plants about. The only movement they should be getting is from the gentle breeze of the fan. Resin on the plants is better than on the arms or the hands.

Larger plants grown for size would have the lower, smaller branches removed when flowering. They hardly produce more than a couple of joints. The idea is to remove them to give more light to the larger branches. Remove only the large older fan leaves that cover or shade any clusters of bud. Spread the branches apart with whatever method you can to attain maximum light coverage. This greatly improves the yield. One large plant in a growing space of say 4 - 6 square foot will give you a larger return than say 4 - 6 smaller plants in the same area. Only the grower knows how they would want to grow and develop the garden.

WASHING OUT

When the plants have been flowering for 5 - 6 weeks it's time to stop feeding them. The reason being that we want a nice smooth smoke with no horrible side tastes. Water the plants only from now onwards (remember p.h.). If you've fed them properly up to now, the leaves should start to yellow from then onwards. This is a natural occurrence. Don't think they need Nitrogen or Epsom salts (see fertiliser section)

F1. cutting in rockwool.
(one week old).

A selection of soil grown plants in different growing stages. Left to right F.I., NL 5 x Haze

Hydroponic grow tank with Swazi, NL5 x Haze and Thai

Thai and Haze in grow block

4 outside plants.
3 NL5 x Haze, AK47 in brown tub

F.I.

CHAPTER 4

Section 2

SEXING THE PLANTS

It goes without saying that if you took your cuttings from a female plant, they too would also be female. However if you've started a handful of seed, you would need to know how to spot the difference between male and female. It's easy. Grow them until they're about 2 - 3 weeks old under constant light. Then cut the light down to a 12 versus 12 light regime. About 14 days later they should all be showing their pre-flowers. In the best instance a female plant will produce 2 little "v" shape stigmas protruding from where the leaf stalks join the main stem. Use a magnifying glass. If these stigmas are in at least 2 - 3 places on the plant you can be reasonably sure they're female.

The male plants produce a little knob or tiny flat growths on small stems. These are hard to tell from females in the beginning, but the two (mostly White) hairs (stigmas) are the best indicator of female gender. As they get older the male plant takes on the appearance of an ornamental flower. Their flowers hang in little bunched clusters resembling small bananas. These clusters are the pods that hold the pollen. They look more like a traditional flower than the females do. Males grow taller and generally more straggly than the females. A couple of weeks before full maturation they elongate and get themselves above the females. Then a few weeks later the females would start to flower. The males pods break open and disperse their pollen all over the females. As in nature, the wind ensures total pollination of all females in the vicinity. The fan does the same in the grow room.

BREEDING

This isn't too hard to do really. With all the seed stock available to the grower it isn't really that necessary to breed your own strain. Unless you're a Martian or something, there's probably a developed strain to suit your personal requirement. However, if you want to have a go, and you've got a couple of strains you would like to try and cross. Here's the easiest way to do it.

Grow the male and female plants in the usual way, keep the male away from the female garden, because the male doesn't need the same amount of light intensity of a female. It can easily be grown on a window-sill or anywhere it can get reasonably adequate light. When the male is ready to cast the pollen, collect it in a small container or whatever. The flowering unfertilised females should be at a point where they are ready to be pollinated. There's no need to pollinate all the females, or even a whole female plant. Don't take the male pollen to the female flowering room. Remove the female that you've selected for pollination from the grow room, (obviously during the light period) and place it on the table.

Using a very fine make-up brush or similar, gently dip it into the male pollen. Dab it carefully over the buds of just one branch. This should give the grower at least a few hundred seeds. Why spoil the rest of the plant to get thousands of seeds? Use a lower branch. This stops pollen falling onto other buds. Spray the pollinated branch with a fine mist spray to ensure that it's stuck to the buds. Wash your hands and put the plant back into the grow room. From now on this plant will go on to produce seed on one branch and *"sensi"* on the rest. You have now produced your own strain (hybrid). Only trial and error will let the grower know if they have produced a successful new strain. Plants react in all different ways. Like any living thing, when cross pollinated it's possible to lose the desired potency of one strain and take on an undesirable characteristic of the other, or vice versa. The strongest genes prevail. Compatibility with a bit of homework will normally help the grower to succeed successfully.

CHAPTER 4

Section 3

SENSIMILLA

Sensimilla is easy to grow. Just keep the males away from them. Sensimilla is the unfertilised female flower. With no male plants to pollinate them, the female flowers go on to produce flower after flower hoping to entice male pollination. These flowers in turn grow into lots of little buds that eventually form together to produce a large resinous head (cola). Sensimilla can be anything from totally useless to devastating. Let me explain. If you grew a plant that was covered in resin it would be easy to assume that these plants would be good. A resinous plant is not an indicator of potency. If the seed stock came from a plant with a very low amount of Cannabinoids in it then they wouldn't have any power (THC) to talk of. Cannabinoids are the chemical compounds in the plant that get you *"stoned"*. Use stock that you have personally evaluated or from a reputable source. This way you will know that you are growing the *"business"*.

Sensimilla is the desired crop for all growers. Seeded bud is not only slightly weaker, it is also a pain to use when you have to keep separating seeds before you can smoke it. A loss of overall return is experienced, because the female has used her energies to produce seed instead of the desired *"virgin bud"*. A waste of time and effort, wouldn't you agree? An unfertilised female will always be better than her *"seeded"* sisters.

CHAPTER 4

Section 4

A BASIC GROWING STUDY

Once the seeds have been germinated, or the cuttings have started to root the real work starts. How you tend your plants from now on determines the end result. A crop that is pest free, and grown in a good environment is half the battle. The other *"half"* consists of your commitment.

All growers want the same result. Plenty of weight combined with the desired *"high"*. This is how I used to go about it. The young plants would be placed as near as possible to the tubes. This will stop them stretching. I wanted plenty of growth right up the stem with very little spacing. To do this I used to water exactly. This stopped the plant from going berserk. In the meantime the root ball was growing away. Hydroponic grow shops sell a liquid hormone designed to promote lots of growth with very little space in between. Highly recommended. I used Maxi-crop root stimulator to help the young plants. Once the plants were about three weeks old, I used to "nip" the top shoot out. This as you know promotes side growth. Now was the time to start feeding *"properly"*. If you are growing a mother plant then she would be fed with a well balanced fertiliser high in **N** (Nitrogen).

Every now and then I would take out a growing tip to promote even more growth. The idea was to promote a "bushy" plant with plenty of potential cuttings. Don't take out too many "tips" because you don't want lots of tiny cuttings. Once the young mother plant was about 6 weeks old I used to stop feeding with nitrogen if I wanted new cuttings, cuttings root easier without an abundance of **N** (Nitrogen). If I was growing a mature plant instead of a cutting, I would have moved the young plant from the tubes and placed it under a sodium light. At about 6 -7 weeks old. Why Sodium instead of a Halide?. All I can personally say is that they grow better. 4 - 6 weeks under the sodium on a 24 hour light duration will bring those plants on so well, you'll be amazed. There is a Sodium lamp available with a spectrum developed for growing and flowering.

Then, when I decided they were big enough to flower, I would switch the light to work the photoperiod. Mature plants grown under light have to be tied into place virtually straight away. This stops the plants intermingling.

Cut away any small straggly branches, they won't give much and the energy is diverted to the larger branches. When I grew fast turnover cuttings, I used to go straight from the tubes to the sodium when they were 6 - 7 weeks old. They were about 9 - 10 inches high, they hadn't been pinched out. I wanted plants that were thick with shoots right up the central stem. Any side branches were removed just prior to going into the flowering room. I ended up with plants a maximum of 15" high, and as thick as milk bottles. 36 of these can be grown in a square metre. They easily return ½ - ¾ ounce each when dried, 18 - 27 OZ from one 400 watt sodium, every 7 - 8 weeks. Add gas (see chapter 6, section 1) and the sky's the limit.

Keep all feeds regular (manual systems). Make sure all the plants requirements are given at the proper time. Find out the exact photoperiod times for your stock to enable you to get the maximum return in the shortest possible time. Overall I don't think that the time and space needed to grow mature plants indoors is worthwhile. Fast turnover cuttings seem to produce comparable weights, and also allows the grower to grow in a smaller space.

I know that lots of cuttings in the system means more work than the fewer (larger) plants but, if all the cuttings were taken at the same time and nurtured in exactly the same way, then overall they would all be the same height and thickness. Growing hydroponically the grower shouldn't really have to get among the plants. Manual gardens can be fed and watered with long spout feeders etc. Larger plants tend to grow a bit erratic when flowering, Smaller, more compact cuttings grow more uniformly. Any leaf removed when the plants are flowering should be taken right at the base. If the humidity is wrong, the little leaf stems left intact turn mouldy. Remove only large shade leaf that covers any *"bud"*. Don't rub the plants to get a *"smell"*, leave the resin on the plant not your fingers.

Plant a couple of garlic plants in with your crop. This is another way that you can help keep down pests. Not really necessary if you've constructed your garden properly, but it's a natural "fail safe". Do what you have to do to ensure that your crop gets the best. In return they'll give you their best. Works both ways, doesn't it? Grow the way that suits you best, but get it right OK.

CHAPTER 5

Section 1

HYDROPONICS

Hydroponics is a way of growing without using soil. You can grow in an amazing variety of mediums. Everything has to be *"spot on"* when growing this way. The water must be about 6.3 - 6.8 P.H. The medium that is used must be able to hold an adequate supply of Oxygen. This is a somewhat delicate way of growing, and any deviation from the "right way" will greatly affect the process. You don't want a medium that will hold on to the feeds. This will cause a *"build up"* and will create lots of deficiencies to come about.

Rockwool is a favourite medium. It can hold the correct amount of feed until the plant has taken it's fill. It allows Oxygen to impregnate it, thus allowing the plant to grow properly. Perlite, Rockwool, clay pebbles, sponge, Sphagnum, Vermiculite to name a few. Although it is better (and cheaper) to buy your own separate nutrients and make your own feeding formulas, because of the precise amounts of feed needed for optimum growth, the plants are unable to easily absorb these because they don't always dissolve well enough.

There are many Hydroponics solutions available, that can be bought over the counter. These are easily absorbed by the plants. Whether you use your own formulas or a ready made feed, there shouldn't be any difference in potency. This is assuming you are preparing and feeding correctly. There are no secret formulas for feeding your plants to make them stronger. Just the right feed with perfect conditions. Grow a *"dud"* plant properly and you'll end up with a perfect *"dud"* plant. The key to high potency lies in the seed. GOOD STOCK = GOOD PLANTS. These formulas when mixed with water have to be checked for their P.H. value. Once you have found out how much P.H. adjuster you have to use

DON'T keep to that amount all the time. The reason being that if you are using tap water, the PH can change drastically when the water source is low. A build up of salts could occur and change the water PH drastically, especially during the Summer and times of drought. This in turn will effect the uptake of nutrient in your plants.

In early growth the plants would need to be fed with a high N.P.K., something like 25-20-15 formula. During middle growth a good feed with less Nitrogen and less of the other 2 major nutrients works best. Say a formula that reads 10-15-10. When it comes to flowering, "up" the phosphorous (P) to about 25-30, the potassium (K) to about 15-20. Unless you are sure that the plants are N deficient (why ?) don't use any Nitrogen at all during flowering. The plants can draw on reserve *"stashes"* of nitrogen to see them through this last stage. As I said in the nutrient section, Yellowing of the leaves is a natural occurrence, An abundance of Yellowing is most probably a Magnesium Sulphate deficiency.

When using ready made shop solutions, you will be buying a feed that is specially calibrated to have the exact amount of nutrient required, also because they are in a fluid form rather than the powder mixes, the plants are able to absorb them easier. How to feed the plants during their life depends on how they are looking and growing. Feed as directed, and in between flush them out with just water (remember P.H.). As long as the plants are a healthy Green, not to many Yellowing leaves (other than those that naturally die anyway). You don't want to keep the plants excessively dark Green. Although they love Nitrogen, too much is unnecessary. A nice *"solid"* Green, with plenty of shoot growth is a sign of a healthy plant.

Hydroponic grow shops these days are well *"clued up"* about this method of growing. Their sales are geared to the Marijuana grower. Hydroponics growing has been used for a few hundred years, only the technology is new, not the idea. Most growers new to the Hydroponics scene are a bit overawed by the equipment you need to have to grow. What way? What system? Flood systems? Hand water system? It all gets a bit confusing. Remember this, both hydroponics and conventional growers are all after the same end product. When the new hydroponics grower sees all the different types of systems available, they are generally at the mercy of the grow shops. They will give you excellent advice as to what way is best. Normally, this means that as well as good advice, they will also be trying to sell you as much as they can. It's only natural, after all they are only shopkeepers trying to make a living. Basically, what they are selling is a system and medium which can grow the plants without soil. Here are a couple of methods the grower could adopt:-

Start the plants (cuttings or seed) in small Rockwool cubes. Hand water/feed these cubes as and how it's needed, once they outgrow the small cubes, place them onto a larger Rockwool cube. These in turn when 'grown on; would be placed onto a slab of Rockwool. Because the Rockwool has the ability to hold both fluid and Oxygen and the texture is perfect for root formation, the growth will be noticeably fast. You can actually see the fluids draining away as they are being used. This keeps the grower on *"the ball"* because they will be visiting the garden regularly.

The same kind of method can be used with the exception that instead of hand watering, the plants could be flooded with fluid from a pump. The pump would be connected to a timer and it would draw fluid from a prepared reservoir tank. The pump would flood the cubes and the excess would be drained away back to the reservoir via a drainage pipe or whatever. Obviously, the plants would be in a tray of some kind. Firstly, switch the pump on and time how long it had to work to adequately water the plants. Then time how long it would be before they were ready to accept another watering. With this you would be able to set the timer on the pump to work accordingly. Never let them dry right out. Take into consideration that you will have to calibrate the flow rate as the plants grow.

Other than adjusting light height and replenishing the

reservoir, this system is virtually automatic. A moist medium for most of the time will help the plant grow a lot better than those that are constantly flooded. Too much water inhibits Oxygen supply. Keep the reservoir topped up, not forgetting to check the P.H. level regularly. Check concentrations of nutrient regularly as well, to maintain proper amounts. There isn't really any room for error with Hydroponic gardens. The slightest deviation from the "norm" can be overcome, but generally to obtain the maximum return from healthy plants, a constant check on all factors must be made. Once you're on top of it, and you fully understand it, this kind of gardening is *"today's gardening"*, fast, efficient, *"ready yesterday"*. As I said earlier in the book, if it were legal to grow, I would do it outdoors, but if I decided for some reason to grow indoors, I would use the Hydroponics system of growing, but I would definitely try to use organic feed as opposed to chemical.

Grow shops sell ready mixed formulas for all stages of growth. Usually, with a trade name, these are generally Grow and Bloom. The grow is normally a complete feed with all vital ingredients for good general growth. The bloom is developed for flowering with no Nitrogen in it. This would have to be supplemented if **N** deficiency occurred during flowering. Some good grow shops are now selling formulas that are organic. Slightly dearer than the others, but in the long run a nicer smoke and bouquet at the end.

A very simple way to construct an efficient Hydroponic set-up would be as follows. Build or buy a water-tight container approximately 48 inches long and 24 inches wide. It would be about 6 inches deep. The top would be fitted inside the container approximately 3 inches down at one end, sloping down to 4 inches at the other. The top should be in one piece, fitting snugly. It should be removable for cleaning purposes. At the lower end of the top, a drainage hole would be made.

The plants would be started in 1 inch rockwool cubes, moving up to the larger grow slabs which, in turn would

A BASIC HYDROPONIC GROW TANK

INLET PIPE

OUTLET PIPE

FILLING/TEST HOLE

3"

PUMP

4"

DRAINAGE AND PUMP INLET HOLES

BED SUPPORTS

RESERVOIR

SLOPING GROW BED

be placed on capillary matting. The matting and grow slabs would be placed on top of the sloping 'bed'. At the top of the sloping bed another hole would be made, in order to be able to replenish the reservoir, and to be able to test the P. H. The tank would be filled with the fertiliser mixture. Using a suitable pump, the mixture would be drawn from the tank via a tube inserted through the lower hole in the grow bed, and up to the top of the of the bed via another tube. The tube would be fixed in a way that allows the fluid to be dispensed evenly around the grow-wool.

Ideally, it would be fixed so that the end of the hose dispensed mid-way across the very top of the grow- bed. An ordinary drinking glass would be placed (upside down) in front of the outlet flow, and this would enable the grower to direct the flow evenly to the growing media. Once the growing media has taken enough fluid on board, the excess will naturally flow down to the bottom of the sloping bed, and back into the tank via the drainage/outlet hole. The pump would be linked to a timer, calibrated to keep the medium in a moist, (not saturated) condition. An external fish-tank pump is perfect for this single tank system.

Don't use clear tubing because this will encourage algae. The tank would also be made lightproof, as would the whole of the top growing surface. Black opaque plastic will do the job for the top. The starter cubes are placed into the main grow slabs via a slit in the black plastic. As long as the whole system is made light/proof then the grower would be unlikely to experience any algae problems. This should be considered when deciding on tank construction. A simple solution would be to use a cut down black water tank from your local plumbing shop. They come in lots of different sizes, so you can pick the one to suit. All you have to do then is buy a similar sheet of black plastic to fit in the top. This is a very simple set-up. Done right, it is one of the most. efficient ways to grow.

CHAPTER 5

Section 2

STARTING A HYDROPONIC GARDEN

Lets assume that we are about to start the Hydroponic garden from scratch. Up to now your plants have been soil grown. It's hard to make the change from one method of growing to another, especially if you are growing successfully in soil. Why change?

Well it's an easier way to grow generally because most of the problems associated with soil growing are eliminated. No *"clogging up"* of the roots, no air restriction and certainly a much cleaner and healthier garden. The plants grow faster because they are able to take in their nutrients when and how they need it.

At this stage, you would either be taking cuttings from your soil grown "mother" or starting from seeds, (see chapter 3, section 3). Firstly soak your 1" starter cubes in the solution you've prepared for feeding the "youngsters". Do this about 24 hours before you need to use them. Cuttings would be taken and dipped into water immediately to stop any air blockages in the stem. This can retard new root growth. Then straight from the water into the Rooting Gel or powder and then placed into the pre-soaked cubes to a depth of about ¾" or 18 mm.

The cubes would then be left in the modules they were purchased in. Cut to size, these modules would be placed in the tray of the propagator, The propagator would be as near to the fluorescent tubes as possible. By doing it this way, all the cuttings are supported in their cubes. Once I tried leaving the solution in the propagator tray in the hope that I wouldn't have to keep going back to replenish it.

After about 10 days, I'd noticed that although the cuttings hadn't died, they hadn't grown. I'd taken about 30 cuttings and every single one of them had callous tissue growing. I realised straight away what I had done. By having enough nutrient solution to feed the plants I was flooding the bottom of the cuttings. They weren't getting enough air. I stupidly thought for some reason , that because rockwool has a capacity to hold onto the oxygen even when soaked, that this would be enough to sustain them. WRONG! I quickly cut the tissue off, and replanted them.

From now on until new roots had shown, I only gave the cubes enough nutrient to keep them moist. This meant visiting the garden twice a day.

Once the 1" cubes were placed into larger cubes (3") I then *"bottom fed"* the plants. They really *"took off"*. With a root system surrounded by a large piece of rockwool, this will feed the roots and supply Oxygen. Remember P.H.

There are lots of different nutrient formulas for cuttings. I found that Maxi-crop root stimulator works as well as anything. Roots appear from the sides and bottom of the 1" cubes in about 7 - 10 days.

Once the roots appear, they must be "potted up" to the next size cube straight away. Lets assume that you have a grow tank the size I have described earlier in this chapter (4' x 2' app.). How may plants do you want to grow? Some growers prefer to grow 1 - 3 fully bushed plants, others like myself prefer 20 single stem cuttings. I found that uniformly grown smaller plants were easier to maintain than the larger ones. Your choice.

Right, back to the cuttings in the larger cubes (3"). These would be placed in trays and moved as near to the tube as possible without burning them. Now you can fill the trays to a depth of 1" or 25m without worrying about it. The roots from the 1" cube will burst through into the 3" cube from all directions. There will be lots of air space above the nutrient level to promote fast healthy growth.

Trim your plants to suit the way you intend growing. If you are only growing 1 - 3 plants in your tank then the need for lots of cuttings is unnecessary. Take the strongest from the mother and discard the rest. Keep a *"mother"* going all the time in your cuttings box.

Once the cuttings have rooted there is no need to use the root stimulator any more. They should now be fed for the first week using a half strength hydroponic solution. Then on to full strength. These plants can be anything from 3 weeks old when putting them into flower. Everything depends on what you want back from them. (Read chapter 3, Containers and Cubes).

The tank would have been prepared to take the new stock. The solution would have been warmed with a thermostatically controlled fish tank heater to about 65 degrees. The P.H. would be tested and adjusted to come into the correct range of 6.3 - 6.8. The growing bed would be covered with a layer of capillary matting.

The plants would be placed in their 3" cubes either directly onto the matting, or onto a larger slab of rockwool.

Single stem plants will be OK in the 3" (75 MM) cubes, but larger multi-branched plants will benefit from extra stability given by the larger slab of rockwool.

A hole would have been made in the grow bed, large enough to accept a measuring stick. Make marks on the stick for every 10 litres, and this will enable you to keep an eye on the nutrient level. All topping up solutions should be kept at the same temperature (approx.) as the grow tank solution. Either buy another heater or keep your *"top-up"* container in your cuttings cupboard (room permitting). NEVER pour freezing water into the reservoir.

RIGHT! The plants are on the mat. The pump would be switched on and the nutrient would be dispersed onto the matting. This in turn would be sucked up by the matting, into the rockwool, straight to the roots. Cover the top of the rockwool to help prevent algae growing.

Check the P.H. daily. If you don't, you could stop the plants from taking in the right amount of nutrient when they need it. How do you know how much food the plants are using? There is a C.F. meter you can buy to tell you this. If you don't get a *"meter"*, then the easiest way to tell is to use your eyes. If you plants are healthy, fast growing, and a nice mid-green, then all is well.

You can change the nutrient solution every couple of weeks to make sure that the plants aren't getting an overdose. A build up of salts in the tank can do this. If you keep a good healthy environment for your plants and you are following the feeding instructions properly, then you shouldn't experience any major problems.

Without a doubt, your first attempt at a "water garden" will be a little wobbly. You will be constantly attending the garden until you find that *"happy medium"*. It's not hard to do, believe me, just different. Get used to it, and once you've got the hang of it, you'll find that you'll be taking more return from the same growing space than you were before.

If you are already a competent soil grower, you'll be *"on top"* of the hydroponic garden very quickly. The novice will take a little longer, but not much.

The warm solution in the tank, combined with the fan for air movement and the thermostatically controlled room heater will ensure that the plants are being grown in ideal conditions. Get these right and you will be "blown away" by your final harvest.

Remember, if you get the growing conditions right, but forget to keep an eye on the P.H. you'll defeat yourself, guaranteed! The P.H. is the most important thing of all. Don't try cutting corners or you'll end up losing the whole crop.

When testing the P.H. always test about half an hour after you've added any new solution. This allows plenty of time for mixing and dispersal through the system, If you haven't got a digital P.H. tester, then a test kit is just as good. Keep the test kit readings in the "green" range.

Growth will be rapid. Use the same knowledge you applied to soil growing to guide you. What I mean by that is, all the positive and negative signs will appear in Hydroponics growing as soil. The difference with "water gardening" is that you have to try your best to get it running properly from the moment you "switch on" because of the plants ability to take up nutrient fast, the P.H. determines what it can take.

Anything outside the acceptable P.H. range will either allow the plants to take up to much nutrient at the wrong time, or not enough. The plants need to be able to take exactly what they need, when they want it. The only way you can do this is to make sure the P.H. is correct. P.H!, P.H!, P.H!, get this in to your head from the start as a priority and you will experience very little hassle.

Adding feed to untreated water will bring the P.H. down. You might find that when you test your 'neat ' water it is outside the acceptable P.H. range but when mixed with the correct ratio of nutrient it could quite easily fall to an unacceptable level.

If not you could use the "up" and "down" to get it right. Your local grow shop will sell all the additives you need to keep your tank running correctly.

There are lots of different ways to grow hydroponically. NONE will be any good if attention to detail is overlooked. If your plants are being fed with the recommended amounts of nutrient and you notice that they are a very dark green, this could be an indicator the solution is too rich. Just add water to dilute the reservoir. If the plants are too light a green, then you can increase the nutrient amount per litre. Obviously, you can only adjust the nutrient strength or dilute it, if you are sure that the P.H. is correct.

For instance, light green plants could easily be judged as being Nitrogen deficient. The wrong P.H. could stop the plants from taking up Nitrogen.

If you haven't checked the P.H. and you feed the plants with more Nitrogen, then when you do get round to adjusting the P.H., the extra strong dose of **N** will quickly be taken up by the plants.

This in turn will make the plants go too dark a green. See what I'm getting at? The secret is to get into a routine of testing and feeding. Once you've done it and got used to it, you will find that this way of growing really is simple.

The C.F. meters I referred to earlier really are essential if you aren't to confident. These will greatly help the gardener to evaluate the plants nutritional needs. Don't worry though if you can't afford one straight away. Many a gardener has grown without a meter and had outstanding results. Just stick to what I've told you and with a few adjustments here and there you will soon overcome any problems.

At the end of every crop the holding tank should be washed out and cleaned thoroughly. The pump and pipe work should be cleaned, As should any filters. A fresh solution (remember P.H.) and new matting will keep your garden in A.1. condition. A week or so prior to the plants maturing, the gardener will want to flush them. This will result in nice Lime green plants with no nutrient residue left in them. Just use water (remember P.H.). The full flavour and bouquet can then be fully appreciated. Lower leaves will turn yellow and start to fall. This is a natural occurrence.

CHAPTER 5

Section 3

GARDEN PESTS

Even if a garden is grown in the most clinical of conditions, there's always a chance that the crop can be *"got at"* by some kind of crawly thing or whatever. Generally, though, a clean properly sealed garden can normally avoid these pests. Cover all ventilation outlets with a very fine mesh. Seal all cracks and holes up. It's amazing that you've made a crack light tight, but a crawly can find its way in. The light spectrum from a Metal Halide attracts pests, as do tubes. With sodium's, they tend to stay clear.

Too high a humidity in the flowering room attracts wood lice and beetles. These don't really hurt the plants, but who wants them anyway? Keep the humidity at the correct level. The biggest enemy for the indoor grower is spider mite. They can destroy your crop. Signs of spider mite are speckle leafs with tiny minuscule holes. This is where they suck the sap out. Once they're established you'll see webs across the branches. If you're not in the flowering stage you can spray them with Bio-Spray Day. This is a safe product. If flowering, do the best you can to keep them down until harvest. It's not the spiders fault it's there. It's yours. How did it get there? Make sure the growing conditions are right, ventilation is correct , and you shouldn't experience any visits from them.

If you collect cuttings from another gardener, they might, unbeknown to themselves and you, have spider mite in the infancy stage. Not noticeable at this point. So home you go and stick them in your stock room. Don't....... At this young stage whether they are infected or not, a spray of the Bio will ensure they're OK. The soil you've got the cuttings in (unless cubes)? Is it bug free? Change it before introducing the plants to yours. Better to sort any impending problems out to begin with, than have to contend with them during serious growth time. Also, never visit another garden and go straight to your own. These spiders are so tiny, you would never know if any were on you.

The fan should help a lot to keep these pests away. Also a spray of fresh water once a week to the underside of the leafs keeps them at bay. They love stagnant, dry conditions, Don't give it them. The ordinary housefly or moth that gets in (probably when you're visiting your garden) wont do much damage if any. None at all once they hit that sticky fly catcher you've hung up. The ordinary household spider wont be a problem either. Whenever I've found one, I've left it. I used to throw a few ladybirds in if they were about. They make sure no living pest *"camps up"* on your plants.

Outside gardens suffer from the same pests as indoors. Green fly being the most common pest. Treat all outdoor gardens like indoor ones. i.e. try to ensure a pest free environment from the start. Pellets to control slugs, Bio-Spray Day for green fly, spraying leaves, good ventilation. Keep on top!

Bud rot is the most horrible thing that can happen, the leafs turn Yellow or Grey, they fall of easily. The middle of the buds turn dark and slimy. If it gets a grip on your stock it will destroy it. If it's gone to far, cut the crop down and start again, salvage what you can. Too high a humidity with inadequate fresh air is the culprit. Your fault OK!

CHAPTER 5

Section 4

DEFICIENCIES (Over fertilisation)

If you're sure that your plants are pest free and they start to show signs of grief, then expect nutrient deficiency. Over fertilisation can give the grower symptoms of deficiency. The plants could have been fed with too much Nitrogen. This *"screws"* the plant up to the point where it cant take anymore. The root system is blocked, It's unable to take in any more fluid and it starts to dehydrate. The soil is wet but the leaves still wilt and eventually die. It's like the equivalent of an overdose. Try washing the soil out with fresh water, remove as much soil as possible from the top of the pots and replace with fresh. Other symptoms are leaf blades curling in to try to save water and circular leaf blades. Feed correctly and eliminate this problem from your garden from the beginning.

NUTRIENT DEFICIENCIES

Nitrogen (N)

Expect to see a gradual yellowing of the bottom leaves with the tips brown and crispy. Growth will be slow and the vegetation will be thin. Mostly on the main stem to begin with. The leaf stems and smaller branches will start to go a purple colour, eventually the whole plant will end up the same. The nice Green colour we want, will take on a very pale Lime Green appearance. Unless you're growing in atrocious conditions, a good general fertiliser, rich in Nitrogen will sort it out in a few days. Nitrogen is used for rapid lush growth. Feed correctly and you won't experience this deficiency. When flowering we don't want the leaf to grow, so we cut it out from the feed at this stage. Then the leaves will start to go yellow and drop off, this is normal.

Phosphorous (P)

It's unlikely that you'll experience a **P** deficiency if you are growing in a decent medium. Symptoms are a dull overall appearance, and plants look to be on the blue/green side. Leaves fall off easily and have a downward curl. If you're feeding correctly the chances are that the problem lies within the soil or water. (Too acid). Sort it out, also leaves can be stunted and slow growing. If your sure it's a **P** deficiency then feed it with a good general fertiliser high in **P**.

Potassium (K)

Once again in a properly fed garden, the grower shouldn't experience a **K** deficiency. Similar symptoms to the **P** occurs. Probably your plants are having trouble taking up their feed. Over toxification of the soil and the wrong water P.H. is probable. Use only water the next couple of times with a drop of washing-up liquid in it. This will help the plant clear it's system and enable it to take up it's next feed easier.

GENERAL

Expect to find all major nutrient deficiencies starting at the bottom of the plant first. The main shade leaves get it first. **P** and **K** deficiencies are unlikely in any good soil that has the correct nutrient content in it. Nitrogen will be the only nutrient that you'll possibly have to keep an eye on. The reason being that **N** is used in large amounts through a plants growing life. To eliminate the **N** problem, feed correctly at the right time. Before you assume that you have nutrient deficiencies make sure there's no problem with the soil or water. If the leaves start to Yellow and you know that you've fed properly, expect Magnesium deficiency. Buy Epsom Salts and apply as directed for a fast recovery.

If you are growing Hydroponically all you'll have to add is an adequate supply of the minor nutrients. If you are using the grow shop formulas, everything you need for optimum growth is in it. When using soil, make sure that it isn't a low grade one. Spend a bit extra on a good, well balanced soil that has an ample supply of all the minor nutrients. Most top brand soils and general growing compost mixtures are a safe bet. The difference in price between these and the low grade mediums is nothing compared to what you get from the end product. Once again, if you are sure that you've fed correctly, the water and soil P.H. is right, then don't expect any problems.

Easier said than done, but honestly, if everything has been taken care of, then what problems can you get? The real problem with any garden, no matter what goes wrong with it, is YOURSELF!!

Don't allow the plants to live in any conditions that can hinder their progress. A lapse in any of these important growing factors, can lead to symptoms of an ailment of some kind. If you haven't got everything correct, then you could end up treating the crop for something totally different to it's real need. That causes more problems to sort out. Don't cut corners.

CHAPTER 6

Section 1

CO_2 (It's a gas)

Assuming that you've grown a garden and you are well happy with the return. Imagine how it would be if you could have 30 - 100 per cent extra. Gas does this. Once again, assuming all other factors are right. CO_2 will greatly improve the overall return. When a plant is in it's light period it will take in the CO_2 available to it and emit Oxygen. During the dark period it will give out CO_2. The more Oxygen they have, the more CO_2 they will make. Even with an adequate fresh air supply, there probably wont be as much CO_2 about for the plants as they would like. Adding extra CO_2 wont improve quality, but it will definitely improve growth (quantity).

You can improve CO_2 with fans and a good ventilation system, but the best way is to get an emitter, sold in all good grow shops. The emitter is fitted to a compressed gas bottle (pubs use them). It is calibrated according to the size of the room. Connected to a timer, the grower can keep the room full of *"grow gas"* constantly. All emitters come with calibration instructions to enable the grower to get it right. The shops will be only too pleased to help you sort it out. They are quite expensive initially and this is what puts most people off using them. Try not to. After going through everything, and getting it all correct, it would be a shame not to use gas. Honestly! You wont be disappointed. You'll be over the moon, guaranteed.

The gas would be dispersed when the exhaust fans are off. It sinks to the bottom of the chamber and gets among the plants. The hot air in the chamber is drawn out through the vents (hot air rises). The timer switches the gas on, dispensing it until the desired amount is present. The fans then turn on to cool the room. Alternate these through the day to maximise saturation. Leaving the door open (if possible) during the light hours will help the grower increase CO_2 if an emitter isn't on the agenda.

Even if you haven't got an emitter, you can still give the plants some help (gas). A bottle of CO_2 with a manual dispenser would be connected to a length of tubing. Drill a hole in the chamber and feed the tube around the plants. Impregnate the tube with holes. Release the gas in between venting the chamber. Not greatly efficient, but it does help to some degree.

CHAPTER 6

Section 2

GENERAL INFORMATION

Mostly, cash is a limiting factor when buying supplies. Use the best available if you can. A min/max. thermometer for the flowering room is essential to be sure that you have the ideal temperatures. The lights and thermostatically controlled heater are combined and calibrated to reach these desired levels. Generally temperatures of about 55 - 60 degrees are ideal for the night period, 70 - 75 degrees during the light period. CO_2 raises the temperature in the room, so adjust accordingly. Try to use a Son-T-Agro light or a Poot. These are highly recommended. Timers for the light system can be the basic ones used for ordinary indoor appliances. Make sure they are capable of taking the power. Check their data with the specifications given with the light.

Timers for gas dispersion will generally be dearer because you need one with quite a few on/off settings. If all your electric requirements are taken from a single source, don't overload it. Check your AMP rating. A good idea is to use circuit breakers between the power source and the equipment. If anything goes wrong then you'll be protecting your investment plus possibly yourself. Imagine coming home to find your home burning because you haven't taken safety precautions. I really hope it doesn't happen to anybody, but it could, take care.

If you have Economy 7 then use this to your advantage and run your system off it. Keep all electric cables fixed away from any water source. A 9" oscillating fan is the smallest you should use. Buy a decent one because the cheap ones seem to pack up when in constant use. When you water your plants, use a watering can with a long nozzle (a piece of hose fitted), to enable you to get to the plants without knocking them about.

Buy a couple of probe testers, one for water, and the

other for soil. These allow you to keep a check on things without mucking about with small test kits. If you have trouble with humidity control in the flowering chamber, you could use a humidifier to control it. These aren't really essential if you get the ventilation system correct. Remember though, if you don't control humidity, this can lead to fungal diseases (bud rot etc.). Sort it out.

CHECK LIST

Below is a check list of essential equipment. Not everything mentioned is vital to produce a quality garden. Try to get the best you can afford. Don't buy inferior equipment to save money. You won't.

When you have the full compliment of growing equipment, you will be able to set the garden up and be virtually guaranteed a top class, full weight garden.

Do the best you can with what you have, and add the *"extra's"* when you can afford them. Then when you get everything working together you will have a garden that is virtually self operational.

1) A good quality light system.
2) An oscillating fan. (Min 9").
3) A timer
4) Circuit breaker.
5) P.H. tester (Digital or kit) for water or soil.
6) C.F. meter. (Highly recommended for Hydro growers).
7) Min/Max. thermometer.
8) A thermostatically controlled room heater.
9) A thermostatically controlled tank heater.
10) CO_2 gas kit.
11) Extractor fan. (Normally for the larger garden).
12) This book. (Highly recommended by me).

Remember, before you buy any of this, there is one crucial thing to get. <u>PROPER STOCK!</u>

CHAPTER 7

Section 1

HARVESTING

This is the time when growers are most excited. Reaping the reward from all the effort put in is the best part. Knowing when to chop the plants down and dry them at their peak can be a bit confusing. The best way to tell is to get a good magnifying glass. An experienced grower wont need one but they will still be looking for the same *"signs"* as the less knowledgeable grower. The plants really start to fatten and bulk up in the last couple of weeks. The desire to get them down and dried is overwhelming. Don't rush things. You've waited long enough, another few days will pay much better dividends if you harvest at the proper time. Be patient!!

You'll have noticed that the buds and all the small leaf in between them are covered in glistening resin. Look closely at them through the magnifying glass and you'll see that the resin is really an abundance of small "glass like" mushrooms. Stigmas (hairs) would be all over the plant, protruding from the buds. When these "hairs" start to die off and go brown this would be an indicator that harvest time is near. WAIT! Go back to the little resin mushrooms and see if they are still standing upright on their little stalks. When they are laying over and the hairs are about 70% brown and withered this would indicate the plants are at their peak. Only the experienced grower would be able to say *"one more day"* or whatever, but generally if you follow this advice you will be as near as is possible without losing out.

Hybrid plants have a tendency to flower at different times from each other. Harvest the ones that are ready and wait a day or two until the others peak. Don't wait until the mushrooms start to fall off. Observe, be patient and reap.

CHAPTER 7

Section 2

DRYING, GRADING, STORING

Once you have decided that the plants are ripe, cut them at the base of the main stem. Hold the plants upside down and from the back remove all the large shade leaves. One plant at a time carefully placing them to one side until all the crop is stripped of their large leaf. Collect all the large leaves together and do what you like with them, they are normally, at their best, a very mediocre smoke.

Starting again, you would cut the branches off in such a way that you leave a *"hook"* to hang them on. Then you would start to remove the smaller leaf that grows around and between the buds. These leaves are normally covered in resin. They are practically as good as the actual bud. It's at this point the grower would make the decision, should I take them right out or cut them as near to the buds as possible? Extra small leaf between the buds will probably slow the drying process a little, but who cares? Either way, save all this small leaf. Put it aside, away from the shade leaf. Use barbers scissors to cut the leaf away. The long blades allow you to get right between the buds.

Place the small resinous leaves on a flat tray and spread them out. The drying room/space would have been prepared. It would be chosen because it's reasonably warm (not hot). Plenty of circulating air to get between the buds, will ensure an even drying out process. Wires or strings would be hung up across the room to take the plants. Too hot a room will dry the plants too quick, and a damp atmosphere could induce mould growth. Drying should take about 4 - 5 days. Any quicker and they will end up brittle and dry. Too long a drying time (7 days plus) probably wont smoke evenly or dry properly. Any loose or small bud would be dried on the flat trays with the small leaf.

A good way to dry those resinous plants is to buy some polystyrene sheeting (1" thick). Instead of leaving a *"crook"* on the branches to hang them by, cut them flush and push them into the polystyrene so that they are standing up. The reason for this is that when the colas are hanging, they naturally *"gravity"* drop down and lay on each other. They end up in tight resinous cola (head). I am not complaining but if you stand them, they dry better because gravity opens them up more and they tend to dry slightly faster. The main advantage being that you won't have to stick your scissors into the head of resin to remove the buds from the stems.

If you use a fan in the drying room to circulate the air, the grower won't experience a harsh smoke from the faster drying time. The air can much easier get between the more open buds then the tightly packed resinous one. Dry the plants in exactly the same way as I previously described for the hanging *"stock"*, and experience an easier manicuring method. The key is to try and think simple. Try to emulate nature. I've tried lots of different experiments with the weed and every time I've had to go back to the very basics. You can't really improve on the natural process. Learn it, follow it and succeed.

When the plants are dry, they would have lost about 85% of their weight. They should feel pliable and sticky. The only moisture being resin. Taking one branch at a time, cut the buds away from their stem and carefully place them in an airtight, lightproof container. Exposure to light can diminish potency. The small leaf and loose bud would be separated. Don't force it into the container. During the manicuring process the scissors and your fingers would be collecting resin. Use a single edged razor blade to carefully remove it, and eventually you will end up with a nice little lump of resin. Keep the scissors clean with alcohol. This will evaporate from any resin taken off. Personal hash?

The small potent leaf can be used to smoke when you have other things to do. In my circle this is referred to as *"daytime"*. As I said earlier, light and air quickly diminish the potency. Find a nice earthenware pot or jar, and store it away in a dark, cool place until needed. Keep it away from light. Don't break it up into small pieces unless you intend smoking it straight away. If you've grown some seed, keep them in a film canister in the fridge.

LAST WORDS

I really hope that I have given you some useful information in this book. My first book GREEN HARVEST was written to show it's reader how to get motivated with very little hassle. I've attempted, in this book to show the reader how to improve their technique in the same way. There is only so much you can write about one subject without bordering on the ridiculous. The real way to grow is to fully understand the basics.

Progress is only attained with enthusiasm. This in itself motivates the grower to become an accomplished cultivator. This book hasn't been written to encourage the reader to grow Marijuana. I don't want you getting into any trouble with the authorities. All I am giving you is information. How you use it, is your business. You're probably only reading this book to learn how to grow when the law changes? Don't get carried away with all the *"hype"* concerning cultivation. It's no big deal and after all, it's only a weed. Probably the best weed in the world though. Be careful, be safe, be happy, and above all, have a fruitful and productive life.

GEORGE MAYFIELD   M.G.F.E.